A *Doonesbury* Book
I Have No Son
by G. B. Trudeau

POPULAR LIBRARY • NEW YORK

I HAVE NO SON

Selected cartoons from

BUT THIS WAR HAD SUCH PROMISE

ALL I HAVE IS A PARASITIC OFFSPRING WHO, YEAR AFTER YEAR, MANAGES TO PASS HIS COURSES JUST IN TIME FOR ME TO SHELL OUT YET ANOTHER FOUR THOUSAND DOLLARS.
SIGH
SON? ME? NO,.. NO, I HAVE NO SON.
GBTrudeau

DAD, I'VE LOOKED OVER YOUR BILL. IT'S RIDICULOUS.
HOW COULD I POSSIBLY PAY YOU $65,251.13? I'VE EVEN ALREADY SPENT NEXT MONTH'S ALLOWANCE.

MOTHER, YOU HAVE BEEN ABSOLUTELY NO HELP IN THIS RECENT MADNESS.

MOTHER, HOW CAN YOU STAND MEEKLY BY AND WITNESS THIS RIDICULOUS CHARADE?!
I'M SORRY, DEAR.

I'M SORRY, DEAR.
MOTHER, I DON'T UNDERSTAND YOU. HOW CAN YOU DEFEND A HUSBAND WHO IS TRYING TO EXTORT MONEY FROM HIS OWN SON?

I'M GETTING A 30% CUT, DEAR.
HEE, HEE.

Accordingly, most problematic solutions are fallible. Mercifully, all else fails; conversely, hope lies in a myriad of polemics.
WHICH PAPER IS THIS?
TAP TAP
GBTrudeau

DUNNO. I HAVEN'T DECIDED YET.
TAP TAP

HA, HA, HA, HA HA! HEE!
HA, HA! HA, HA, HA! HEE, HEE!

FOR A LIBERAL, YOU'RE PRETTY LOVABLE.
THANKS.
GBTrudeau

I'M NOT SURE I UNDERSTAND IT EITHER, RUFUS. BUT IT SURE IS GREAT! WHERE ELSE BUT IN AMERICA COULD A MAN BE PAID $175,000 FOR GROWING 22,000 ACRES OF WEEDS?!

MY COUNTRY 'TIS OF THEE, SWEET LAND OF SUBSIDY!!
GBTrudeau

CHATTER! CHATTER, CHATTER... CHATTER, CHATTER, CHATTER! CHATTER, CHATTER, YES, CHATTER!.. CHATTER, CHATTER AND CHATTER.
...AND IN CONCLUSION-LET ME JUST SAY-CHATTER!
© G.B. Trudeau

THIS CONCLUDES OUR REGULAR BROADCAST DAY. STAY TUNED FOR THE NATIONAL ANTHEM, FILM CLIPS OF THE MARINES, AND A STORY FROM THE LIFE OF JESUS.
OH, SAY CAN YOU S-E-E-E..

NOW, MOM, BEFORE YOU GET UPSET, LET ME EXPLAIN. I... WHAT, MOM?...

SHE WANTS TO JOIN US.
GBTrudeau

WELL, BERNARD, WILL YOU LOOK AT THAT?
A PUDDLE!.. WHAT'S A PUDDLE DOING OUT ON A SUNNY DAY LIKE THIS?

IT MUST BE A SPRING-FED PUDDLE!
IMAGINE! A SMALL BODY OF WATER RIGHT ON OUR OWN PROPERTY!

WELL, OF COURSE! ALL THE GREAT COMMUNES HAVE OVERLOOKED SMALL BODIES OF WATER!
WHAT'LL WE CALL IT?
WALDEN PUDDLE.

MICHAEL, I CAN'T TELL YOU HOW DELIGHTED I WAS TO DISCOVER WALDEN PUDDLE! RIGHT HERE ON OUR OWN PROPERTY!

YOU KNOW, I'LL BET I'M THE FIRST HUMAN-TYPE TO LAY EYES ON THAT PUDDLE! WHAT A PUDDLE! WET AND WILD, AND UNPOLLUTED TO BOOT! MAN, I FELT LIKE MAGELLAN, OR CORTÉS, EVEN.

C'MON ZONKER, A PUDDLE'S A PUDDLE.
WELL, YOU CAN SAY THAT, OF COURSE, BUT I'M SURE OF ONE THING ABOUT WALDEN..

..IT'S NOT YOUR RUN-OF-THE-MILL PUDDLE.
©GBTrudeau

AS AN EARLY RISER WALKS ALONG THE BEACH, HE SPOTS A FEW BUBBLES FAR OUT TO SEA..

WHAT CAN IT BE BREAKING THE STILL WATER OF THE EARLY MORN? A CROWD OF PEOPLE QUICKLY FORMS!

Dear Rev. Berrigan;
I've been meaning to
write you for sometime
about this Kissinger
kidnapping business. I
want to offer my services
on your second attempt.

TAP TAP

I've got this great, evil
Kidnap plan that's bound
to work. Once we get him
kidnapped, we can leave
him here at the commune
where I live. One of my
best men, Didi Robins
will guard him until the
ransom is paid.

TAP

WELL, FOR ONE THING, I DIG HER INTERVIEWS, DIDI.

HMM.. O.K. I'LL PUT HER ON OUR FAN LETTER LIST.

Ms. Barbara Walters
c/o Mass Media
N.Y.C., N.Y.

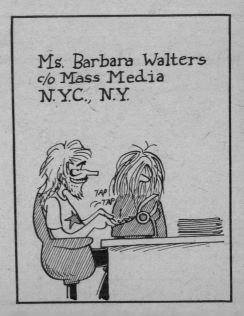

TAP TAP

WELCOME TO MY FAMILY'S FIFTH FLOOR WALK-UP! IT IS HERE THAT IS HOUSED MY PRIVATE GHETTO ARTIFACTS COLLECTION.

MY COLLECTION IS CONSIDERED BY MOST GHETTO CRITICS TO BE ONE OF THE FINEST IN THE CITY... FIRST OF ALL,... AN ACTUAL EVICTION NOTICE!

WOW.

GEE!

AND HERE, MY FRIENDS, A COURT SUMMONS AND A NICKEL BAG!
OH, NO, REALLY?
FASCINATING! JUST FASCINATING!

A CANCELLED WELFARE CHECK!
FANTASTIC!
RIGHT ON!

DID YOU HEAR THAT MIKE? DID YOU HEAR WHAT RUFUS SAID? BEFORE THE NIGHT'S OUT, THERE'S GOING TO BE A ROBBERY IN THIS CITY!

FOR GOSH SAKE, MIKE, DO SOMETHING!
©GBTrudeau

IF YOU'LL LOOK ACROSS THE STREET, YOU'LL SEE A GROUP OF MIGHTY EVIL LOOKIN' YOUNG AFRO-AMERICANS.

THESE GUYS ARE THE BAD DUDES OF THE NEIGHBORHOOD—THE GUYS WHO ARE FED UP WITH BEING TREATED, WITH CONTEMPT, SCORN, AND HATRED BY A RACIST WHITE SOCIETY.

DUM-DE DUM-DE DOO!
WHAT'S FOR DINNER, ZONKER?

MACROCHAOTIC SALAD! FRESH FROM LE GARDEN..
M-M-M GOOD, FOLKS!
ZONKER, THE LETTUCE IS DIRTY!

WHEN MY WHEAT REACHES MATURITY, I'LL MAKE BREAD, AND CAKES... PIES! DINNER ROLLS!..

CROISSANTS!
NO!

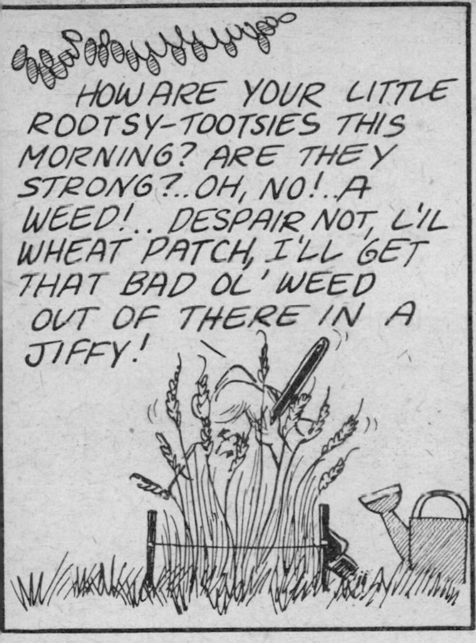
HOW ARE YOUR LITTLE ROOTSY-TOOTSIES THIS MORNING? ARE THEY STRONG?..OH, NO!..A WEED!.. DESPAIR NOT, L'IL WHEAT PATCH, I'LL GET THAT BAD OL' WEED OUT OF THERE IN A JIFFY!

ONE CANNOT BE TOO GOOD TO ONE'S WHEAT PATCH.

ISN'T IT AMAZING HOW MUCH ZONKER'S BECOME INVOLVED WITH HIS GARDEN?
IT CERTAINLY IS. I MUST SAY, I'M VERY SURPRISED..
YOU KNOW HE SPENDS ALL DAY OUT THERE WITH HIS BRUSSELS SPROUTS AND PAPRIKA PLANTS.

ZONKER, WHERE ARE GOING WITH THAT BOWL OF SCRAMBLED EGGS?
I'VE GOTTA FEED MY WHEAT PATCH.

YOU CAN'T BE SERIOUS.
I'M SERIOUS, I'M SERIOUS. MY WHEAT PATCH HASN'T HAD BREAKFAST YET...

HE SO WANTED
TO BE PART
OF THE RESIDUAL
FORCE.

GEORGE, WOULD YOU PLEASE EXPLAIN THIS CRAZY WAR TO ME? I DON'T GET IT!—A BUNCH OF HARVARD GRADUATES THOUGHT UP THIS WHOLE WAR...

...BUT THEY SEND A BUNCH OF DRAFTED HIGH-SCHOOL GRADUATES TO FIGHT IT! FINALLY, THEY GET A GUY, ME, WHO WANTS TO STAY, AND THEY WITHDRAW HIM! IT'S JUST NOT FAIR!

WELL, SURE IT'S UNFAIR! ALL WARS ARE UNFAIR.
I KNOW, I KNOW!..

..BUT THIS WAR HAD SUCH PROMISE!!

THE COLD WAR'S A WHOLE DIFFERENT SCENE, PHRED! WHO KNOWS, MAYBE I'LL GET TO FIGHT THE KRAUTS!

WE GOOKS ARE GOING TO MISS YOU, B.D.
©GBTrudeau

MAN! OL' B.D. COMING HOME! IT'S ENOUGH TO GIVE A FELLOW REAL CAUSE FOR JOY!

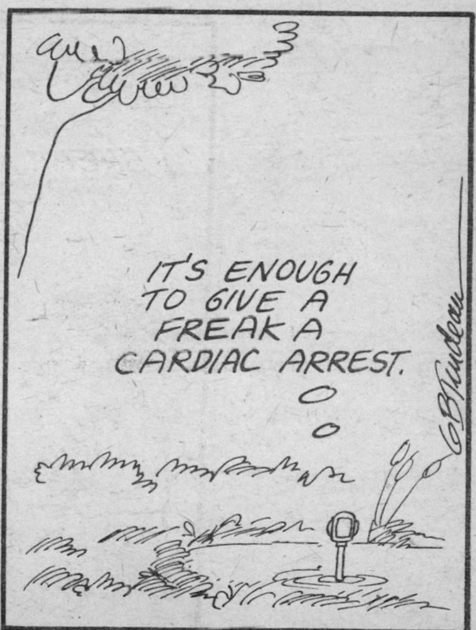
IT'S ENOUGH TO GIVE A FREAK A CARDIAC ARREST.
GBTrudeau

GET OUT OF HERE, ZONKER, I'M WARNIN' YOU!
NONSENSE, CAP'N! WE GOT LOTS OF STUFF TO CATCH UP ON!

I'M GONNA COUNT TO THREE!
SO HOW YA BEEN?
GB Trudeau

THAT'S WHAT I WANTED TO TALK TO HIM ABOUT! SOMETHING **TERRIBLE** HAS HAPPENED!

EVAPORATED!

YOU LUCKY LITTLE DEVIL! I'M STILL LOOKING FOR A SUMMER JOB! WHAT ARE YOU GETTING?
$1,300. A WEEK.
YES, OPERATOR, I'D LIKE TO REVERSE THE CHARGES ON THAT CALL.

GO RIGHT IN, GENTLEMEN, YOU'RE EXPECTED.
THANKS.

GOOD AFTERNOON, SIRS. THIS IS RUFUS JACKSON, AND I'M MIKE DOONESBURY, HIS ADVISOR AND FRIEND.
YOU'RE RUFUS JACKSON?

I'D LIKE TO TALK TO MR. WILLIAM MERRIAM, PLEASE..... TELL HIM THAT ACE REPORTER ZONKER HARRIS IS CALLING..

...HELLO, MR. MERRIAM?.. THIS IS ZONKER HARRIS, MILD-MANNERED MUCKRAKER FOR THE CAMPUS NEWS! LISTEN, I'VE GOT SOME IT&T MEMOS HERE REGARDING A NIXON CORONATION. ANY COMMENT?..

...NOW DON'T BE LIKE THAT, BILL! YOU KNOW ALL ABOUT THE NIXON MONARCHY, BABY! THE MEMOS ARE SIGNED BY YOU! WE'VE GOT THE GOODS ON YOU, BILL... WHAT?..

HE SAYS IT'S GOING TO BE A CONSTITUTIONAL MONARCHY.

WELL, MIGHT AS WELL GET GOING ON THESE MEMOS.
LET THE TRUTH HANG OUT, BROTHER.

"NOVEMBER 2 MEMO RE: NIXON CORONATION. TOM: I TALKED TO DICK TODAY AND HE'S VERY EXCITED ABOUT BEING CROWNED KING RICHARD I."
TAP TAP

"I TOLD DICK'S PEOPLE WE WOULD HELP CONVERT THE UNITED STATES INTO A KINGDOM. DICK ASKED WHAT WE WANTED IN RETURN. I INDICATED WE NEEDED ADDITIONAL PROPERTY FOR OUR GROWING CONCERNS."
TAP
TAP

"HE PROMISED US THE MOON."
AND HE CAN DELIVER!
TAP

AND NOW...
...ANOTHER MEMO!

"NOVEMBER 4
RE: FAMILY REACTION.
SO FAR IT WOULD SEEM THAT THE NIXONS ARE DIVIDED IN THEIR REACTIONS TO THE CORONATION IDEA."
TAP TAP